Oliver Twist

Charles Dickens

Academic Industries, Inc.
West Haven, Connecticut 06516

ISBN 0-88301-757-1

Published by
Academic Industries, Inc.
The Academic Building
Saw Mill Road
West Haven, Connecticut 06516

Printed in the United States of America

about the author

The most popular, and perhaps the greatest of English novelists was Charles Dickens. Born in 1812, Dickens was the son of a clerk in the Navy-Pay office.

Although from a poor background, Dickens was both ambitious and industrious. His education came from books, those in school as well as his own. He wrote of people as he saw them and created some of the most timeless characters in literature.

The turning point in his life came at the time of his marriage. Both his wedding day and his first publication occurred in the same year. From that time, he continued to write many novels during the conventional Victorian era.

One of his most famous works is *A Tale of Two Cities*. This novel is a serious and sensational experiment in historical romance. It has a dual theme: love and death, and what effect they have on the novel's characters. *Oliver Twist*, on the other hand, is mainly a story of goodness rewarded. Its picture of life in the London slums is truly striking.

Oliver Twist

Charles Dickens

Fagin

Nancy

Bill
Sikes

Mr.
Brownlow

Oliver Twist

Monks

Rose
Maylie

During the 1800s, many poor people in England lived in buildings called workhouses. Men, women, and children lived in separate buildings. Oliver Twist was born in one of these.

Let me see the child and die.

Don't talk of dying yet, my dear!

She's gone, nurse. Who was she?

No one knows. She was found lying in the street last night. Someone brought her into the workhouse.

At least the child is healthy. But his poor mother. . . .

When nothing could be learned about his mother, the boy was named Oliver Twist by the beadle, head of the workhouse.

Mrs. Mann sure got angry when we asked for more food.

But I was hungry.

We're always hungry or cold or sick.

One day Oliver and two other boys were being punished in the coal cellar in the children's workhouse when Mr. Bumble, the beadle, arrived. Oliver was quickly cleaned up and taken upstairs.

Well now, Oliver. I've come for you. You're nine years old today, and it's time you went to work.

Yes, sir.

At the next workhouse, Oliver was taken before the board, a group of about eight men in charge of the poor. Oliver was too frightened to speak.

What's your name, boy?

Do you say your prayers?

You'll start work picking oakum tomorrow.

Take him to bed.

What's picking oakum?

Pulling ropes apart for twelve hours a day!

We get three dishes of oatmeal a day. We get an onion twice a week, and on Sunday we get half a roll.

Go to sleep!

When Oliver had been in the workhouse for about three months, one of the boys grew angry about the food.

I'm hungry! If I don't get one more dish of oatmeal every day, I'll start eating people!

He means it!

One of us will have to ask for more tomorrow.

Oliver was chosen.

Please, sir. I want some more.

No one could believe what Oliver had said. The cook rushed to tell the beadle, Mr. Bumble. Mr. Bumble rushed to tell the board. The board was terribly angry.

He asked for *more?*

Lock him in a room alone, Mr. Bumble. Put a notice on the gate. We'll give a reward to anyone taking him off our hands.

A chimney sweep was interested in getting the reward.

The boy's small. But cleaning chimneys is dangerous work.

Only if they are careless.

Oliver was taken before two judges who would decide whether he could be given to the chimney sweep.

Please, sirs, don't let that man take me away.

Bring this boy back to the workhouse, and treat him kindly.

11

It was next decided that Oliver would be apprenticed to Mr. Sowerberry, the undertaker. This meant that Mr. Sowerberry could keep him for seven years.

He's very small, but he'll grow.

Yes, he will. Get downstairs, little bag of bones.

Here's the new boy, Charlotte. You don't mind eating out of the dog's dish, do you, boy?

No, ma'am.

When Oliver had finished every scrap of food in the dog's dish, Mrs. Sowerberry took him upstairs.

This is where you'll sleep. Under the counter.

Oliver woke up the next morning hearing a loud knocking on the door.

Did you want a coffin, sir?

Don't you joke with me, workhouse boy. I'm Mister Noah Claypool, who works for Mr. Sowerberry. So you work for me.

Charlotte always gave extra food to Noah and laughed when he teased Oliver.

Oh, Noah. Why don't you leave the boy alone?

Leave him alone? Everyone leaves Oliver alone— even his parents.

Mr. Sowerberry liked Oliver. He gave him a cane and a long hatband for his high hat. Oliver led the funeral processions.

That boy! Isn't he wonderful?

Such a beautiful funeral!

Noah was unhappy to see the new boy given such an honor. So he treated Oliver worse than ever.

Don't you dare say anything about my mother!

You're lucky she's dead. She was a bad person.

Oliver grabbed Noah and shook him. Then he knocked the older boy to the floor.

Help! Help! Oliver's killing me!

Charlotte and Mrs. Sowerberry rushed in and started hitting Oliver. Noah joined them.

You terrible child—trying to kill poor Noah! We'll send for the beadle.

Alone in the workshop, Oliver gathered up his few extra clothes. Just as the sun rose the next morning, he quietly opened the door and left for good.

Oliver hurried at first, fearing someone would come after him. But as he became tired and hungry, he slowed down.

One day a week later, Oliver sat resting on a doorstep. A strange-looking boy came up and stared at him.

I'm tired and hungry. I've been walking for seven days.

You shall have food or I'm not Jack Dawkins.

The strange boy bought Oliver some food. He talked to Oliver as he ate.

I am friends with an old gentleman who lives in London. He'll give you a place to stay.

Oliver didn't like what he saw of London as he and Jack Dawkins ran through the back alleys. The city was dirty, smelly, and full of noisy people—even at midnight.

Suddenly Jack pulled Oliver through a doorway and up a dark staircase.

This is him, Fagin—my friend, Oliver Twist.

I am happy to meet you, my boy. Here, have some sausages. And have a hot drink!

Oliver wanted to think about this strange place. But the food, the drink, and the friendly people were too much for him. He fell fast asleep on one of the floor mats.

The next morning when Oliver awoke, only Fagin was in the room. He was going through a box filled with jewels.

Ah, lovely!

What are you staring at, boy?

Please, sir, may I get up now?

Of course. Go and wash up.

When Jack and Charley Bates arrived, the jewel box was nowhere to be seen.

After breakfast, Jack and Charley played a strange game with Fagin.

Have you been hard at work, boys?

Very hard. We have some wallets, some kerchiefs, and a ham.

Now watch closely, Oliver. I am a gentleman looking in store windows. See, in my pockets I have my watch, a snuff box, and a handkerchief.

The boys darted in and out as Fagin moved around the room. When he stopped, the boys held out their hands. Oliver gasped at what he saw.

There, Oliver. See what they've found? If I feel them taking anything, we have to start over. See how well Jack wins? We call him the Artful Dodger.

17

After the boys had left, Fagin played the game with Oliver.

Now, my boy. See if you can take out my handkerchief without my knowing it.

Here you are, sir.

You're a clever boy, Oliver. I didn't feel it.

For many days Oliver stayed in Fagin's room. Sometimes he joined the boys in their game.

Please, sir, may I go out with the others?

Soon, my boy. Soon.

Sometimes there was much to eat and sometimes very little. Sometimes Fagin was kind, but he could also be cruel.

Lazy boys who come home empty-handed go to bed without supper!

At last Fagin let Oliver go out with Charley Bates and the Artful Dodger.

Oliver couldn't understand how the boys worked. They seemed to be just walking along the street having fun.

Charley stole some fruit!

Sh-h-h-h! Just watch!

Then Oliver saw the two boys cross the street and stand next to an old gentleman. As the gentleman picked up a book, the Dodger took his handkerchief.

Suddenly the gentleman found that his handkerchief was gone! Oliver was so frightened that he began to run. "Stop thief!" shouted the gentleman and ran after Oliver. Soon many others had joined him, including Charley and the Dodger.

Stop thief! Stop thief!

Oliver was easily caught. He was taken to jail.

Even if you're not sure about him, sir, he'll have to go before the judge.

But there's something about that boy that reminds me of someone.

Oliver was brought before Mr. Fang, a very strict judge.

What are you saying, Mr. Brownlow?

The boy, sir— he looks ill!

The boy is ill? Not at all. He's faking. Now, no one saw him steal, and nothing was found on him? I don't believe it. I sentence him to three months in jail.

Oh, please! No!

Just then an old man rushed into the court.

Stop, please! I couldn't come any sooner. I saw Mr. Brownlow robbed by two other boys. This child was just watching!

Hearing this, the judge had to let Oliver go. Then Mr. Brownlow ordered a coach and took him to his home in Pentonville.

Where am I? Who are you?

You've been very sick. I'm Mrs. Bedwin, Mr. Brownlow's housekeeper.

When Oliver was better, Mrs. Bedwin took him downstairs.

The lady in that picture seems to talk to me.

She's lovely, but I don't know who she was. I'll just turn your chair so the picture won't bother you.

Ah, here's Mr. Brownlow!

Thank you, sir, for all you've done for me.

We're happy you're better, Oliver. But I can't believe how much you look like the lady in the picture!

While Mr. Brownlow and Mrs. Bedwin were worrying about Oliver's health, his old friends were worrying for a different reason.

You should have seen him, Fagin. He was bouncing off buildings like a rubber ball.

Where's the boy now?

Speak out or I'll kill you!

Why, he got caught. He's in jail!

Just as Fagin threw some beer, Bill Sikes walked in.

Sorry, Bill, but we've had some trouble. Oliver is in jail. If he talks, it will be bad for us.

Then we must get him out. Here's Nancy. She'll do it.

Go to the police? Not me!

She'll go. I'll make her do it!

Here, my dear. Take this clean apron and covered basket. And carry a large house key.

So Nancy marched down to the jail and put on a very good show for the officer at the gate.

My brother Oliver Twist! My poor little brother! I *must* see him!

Why, he was sick. A gentleman took him away in a coach. But I heard him tell the driver to go to Pentonville, just outside London.

When Nancy returned, Fagin called a meeting.

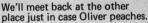

The police haven't been here, so Oliver hasn't peached on us yet. But we must get him!

We'll meet back at the other place just in case Oliver peaches.

Meanwhile, a man named Mr. Grimwig visited his old friend, Mr. Brownlow. Oliver met the gentleman.

Oliver, take these to the store and bring me back the change.

I'll be right back, sir.

That boy has a new suit, books, and money. He'll go back to the thieves, I'm sure.

As it happened, Oliver did go back to the thieves, but not because he wanted to. Nancy and Bill Sikes had caught sight of him.

Help! I don't belong to them!

You bad child! You'll come home to your mother right now. And you've been stealing books!

Poor Oliver didn't have a chance. Bill grabbed the books, and he and Nancy dragged the boy off to Fagin.

Oh, I'll die laughing! Look at his clothes, Fagin!

Glad to see you are looking so well, my boy. We'll give you another suit so you won't spoil your Sunday best.

Look here! Money!

I'll take it. You keep the books, Bill.

No. It's mine, old man, for the trouble of getting the boy back.

Please send the books and money back to Mr. Brownlow. He'll think I stole them.

Ah, that he will, Oliver. That's just what we want him to think.

So Oliver made a dash for the door. Fagin and the boys ran after him.

Keep back the dog, Bill. He'll tear the boy to pieces.

Get out of the way, Nancy!

Bill pushed the girl away. Just then Fagin and the boys grabbed Oliver.

Wanted to call the police, did you, my boy? Well, we'll soon cure that.

Don't hit him, Fagin!

I'm sorry I brought the boy back. You made a thief of me. Now you're going to make a thief of him. But you don't have to hurt him, too.

Ah, women! Charley, take Oliver to bed.

Fagin knew many ways to handle Oliver. He told him stories of other boys who had gone to the police—and had been hanged. He often left Oliver alone to think about those stories.

Soon Oliver was glad to be playing the game again.

Meanwhile, Mr. Bumble, the beadle, had come to London on business. After reading an offer of a reward for news of Oliver Twist, he hurried to Pentonville.

Your report shows that Oliver is a troublemaker. Never let me hear the boy's name again!

I will not believe that the boy is bad!

In a very different kind of room, Fagin was visiting Bill Sikes.

When Nancy went to get Oliver, she showed him some bruises on her neck.

For the job in Chertsey we'll need a very small boy.

Well, it's time Oliver earned his keep. He'll do whatever you want.

I've tried to help you before. But if you don't do what Bill says, he'll hurt us both. Now hurry.

It took Bill and Oliver two days to reach Chertsey. Bill's partner, Toby Crackit, was waiting for them.

It was two o'clock in the morning. As they crept up to a large house, Oliver knew the men planned to rob it.

Toby put his hand over Oliver's mouth and dragged him to the house.

Oliver, take this lantern. I'll open that window and put you inside. Go up to the stairs and open the outside door for us.

Once inside, Oliver tried to warn the people sleeping in the house. But two men appeared at the top of the stairs. There was a flash, a loud noise, and Oliver fell backwards.

Quick! The boy's been hit! Help me get him out, Toby!

28

The next day, knowing nothing of Oliver's troubles, Mr. Bumble, the beadle, visited Mrs. Corney, head of the women's workhouse.

During their visit, someone knocked on the door.

> Please come, ma'am. Sally is dying, and she has something to tell you.

Grumbling, Mrs. Corney went to Sally's room. She shut the door, leaving the two nurses outside.

> In this very room, I once took care of a pretty young woman. She gave birth to a boy, and then she died.

> What about her?

> I robbed her. It was hanging 'round her neck when she died. Gold, it was.

> Go on! What was it? Who was she?

> She asked me to keep it safe for her boy. They called him Oliver. The gold I stole was. . . .

But Sally could say no more. Falling back, she died.

Leaving the room, Mrs. Corney let the nurses in again.

She's dead. She had nothing to say after all.

Meanwhile, Mr. Bumble had been behaving in a strange manner. He looked in all the closets and drawers.

When Mrs. Corney returned, Mr. Bumble lost no time telling her why he had come.

Ma'am, I'm to be the new master of the workhouse. Let us get married and share our lives and work with each other!

Why, yes. Thank you, sir.

A little later, Mrs. Corney told Mr. Bumble that Sally had died.

I knew something was wrong, my love. Was that it?

I'll tell you more about it after we're married.

While these things were taking place in the workhouse, Fagin was still waiting for Bill Sikes and Oliver to return.

Soon Toby Crackit arrived.

This is my first meal in three days! Now—how's Bill?

What! I thought *you* knew where they were!

Well, I don't. They shot the boy. We dragged him between us, Bill and me. When they kept coming —with guns and dogs—we dropped the boy in a ditch. Then we ran.

Fagin rushed out to Sikes' house. Nancy was there alone.

Where's Bill? Where's Oliver? That boy's worth a fortune to me!

I don't know anything. I don't know what you're talking about. Go away.

Returning home, Fagin found a man waiting for him.

Where have you been?

Hello, Monks. I've been out on business.

It's as dark as a grave in here.

We never leave lights on. A candle will light us to the room upstairs. The boys are locked in downstairs.

Why didn't you make a pickpocket out of Oliver?

It didn't work. He was different from the other boys. But he may be dead now anyway.

If he *is* dead, remember that it's no fault of mine. What's that? A woman passed by!

No one's there, Monks. You worry too much.

Just to be sure, they checked the house. Finding nothing, Monks left.

That same day, the two servants who had chased the robbers were telling their story to the cook and the maid when there came a knock at the door.

Here's the thief!

He's hurt! Take him inside, Giles.

I'll run and tell Mrs. Maylie.

Mrs. Maylie, the lady of the house, sent for the doctor. Then she and her niece, Rose, waited for his report.

Will you ladies follow me, please. The thief is dirty, but he does not look very evil.

Mrs. Maylie and Rose were surprised to find that the thief was a small boy. After hearing Oliver's story, they were filled with pity for him.

Dear aunt, do not send this child to prison!

Of course not! Doctor, we must try to help him!

The doctor went to tell the servants, Giles and Brittles, to change their stories. But when he reached the kitchen, a police officer was there.

A boy is here who came to us hurt this morning. Are you going to swear he's the same boy that you—in one moment— saw climb through the window last night?

I can't *swear* it, sir. No indeed.

After a while, the officer decided that the robbery had been done by experts, not by Oliver. And so the happy Maylies took the boy to the country for the summer.

I've never been so happy—except at Mr. Brownlow's.

On one of his visits, the doctor took Oliver to see Mr. Brownlow. But the house was for rent, and the people had left England.

Then one night a few months later, Rose Maylie became ill.

Quickly, Oliver. Go to the inn and have them send for the doctor.

Oliver did so at once. But as he turned to go home, he stumbled against a stranger.

I beg your pardon, sir.

You! What the devil are you doing here?

Oliver soon forgot the stranger's odd words because he was worried about Rose. One day soon after, as Oliver was gathering flowers for her, a coach stopped beside him. A young man called out.

Oliver! What news of Miss Rose? Mr. Harry and I have just come from Chertsey.

Dr. Losberne says she is no longer in danger.

Oh, that is good to hear!

Oliver was very happy with the Maylies. Then one day as he was studying, he looked up and saw two faces at the window. They were Fagin and the stranger from the inn.

Yes. That's Oliver.

Did you think I wouldn't know that boy?

Harry Maylie came running when Oliver screamed. But he found no trace of the two men.

A few days later, Harry Maylie asked Rose a question.

Rose, dear, I love you. Will you marry me?

I cannot marry you, Harry. You will be an important man someday, and the shame of my family will hold you back.

Harry was very sad that Rose would not marry him. But Mr. Bumble became upset because Mrs. Corney had married him!

First I got married. Then someone else became the beadle.

I am the one who should be angry!

Mr. Bumble went off to a bar to get away from his wife. There a man spoke to him.

My name is Monks. Weren't you the beadle here at one time?

Yes, I was.

Well, I'll pay you for some information. Twelve years ago a young woman gave birth to a boy in the workhouse. This boy later worked for a coffinmaker. Then he ran away to London.

Oliver Twist!

I don't care about Oliver. I want news of the old woman who took care of the mother.

Ah, Sally. She died last winter. But I know someone who was with Sally when she died.

How well Mr. Bumble remembered the night Sally died! It was the night he had asked Mrs. Corney to marry him.

Late that night, Mr. and Mrs. Bumble met with Monks in an empty warehouse.

First, how much will you pay?

Here. It's gold.

All right. Before Sally died, she told me she had stolen something from the woman that she had promised to keep for the boy. Then she died.

Here is what Sally had. Inside this bag is a gold locket and a gold wedding ring. The ring has "Agnes" written inside.

Monks took the bag, pulled up a trap door in the warehouse floor, and dropped the bag through the hole.

There! Everything has gone to the bottom of the river.

Meanwhile, Bill Sikes had been very ill. Nancy had been taking care of him.

Oh, Bill. Now *I* don't feel well.

Oh, shut up! What? She's fainted!

Just then Fagin, Charley Bates, and the Dodger walked in.

Ah, the dear Nancy's fainted. Dodger, give her a drink. Charley, give her some fresh air.

There, my dear. See all the things we've brought.

Where have you been for so long? What I need is money.

I'll send the Dodger with some tonight.

No! I'll send Nancy for it.

39

While Nancy waited at Fagin's for the money, a man came up the stairs calling for Fagin. The voice surprised Nancy. It was Monks.

The girl is just one of my young people. We'll go upstairs. Nancy can stay here.

Quickly, Nancy took off her shoes and crept upstairs after them to listen.

When Fagin came back, Nancy was again at the table as he had left her.

Why, my dear, how pale you look.

I don't feel well, and I'm tired. Give me the money and let me get back.

That night Nancy drugged Bill's drink. When he fell asleep, she put on her shawl and left.

Hurrying through the London streets, Nancy entered a family hotel in a good part of London.

You want to speak to Miss Maylie? Alone? No, you must leave!

Please! It's important!

Rose Maylie agreed to see the visitor, so Nancy was taken upstairs.

Please listen closely. I'm the girl that dragged Oliver Twist back to old Fagin's when he was in Pentonville.

From the time I was a child, I've known only cold and hunger. I'd be killed if they knew what I'm about to tell you. Do you know a man named Monks?

No, I don't.

Well, Monks knows you. And I heard him telling Fagin that he knows Oliver, too. He made a deal with Fagin to turn Oliver into a thief.

Tonight I heard Monks tell Fagin, "The only things that can prove who Oliver really is have been thrown into the river." Monks said he's got all his brother's money now, but that he'd rather Oliver rotted in jail as a thief.

His brother? I must know more!

Every Sunday night, very late, I'll be on London Bridge.

You have risked your life coming here. Let me give you money or help you find a new life.

It is too late for that, dear lady. There is one I cannot leave, bad as he is. But we will meet again.

The next morning Oliver rushed in to tell Rose that Mr. Brownlow was in London. Giles had his address. So Rose decided to take Oliver there at once.

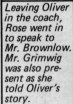

Leaving Oliver in the coach, Rose went in to speak to Mr. Brownlow. Mr. Grimwig was also present as she told Oliver's story.

Ah, so he missed us? But where is he?

He is waiting in the coach.

Mr. Brownlow rushed out and soon brought the happy Oliver into the house. He rang for Mrs. Bedwin.

Now put on your glasses, Mrs. Bedwin. See if you can find out why I wanted you.

Oh, Mrs. Bedwin!

My dear Oliver! Ah, I knew he'd come back. Look how he's grown!

While Mr. Grimwig, Mrs. Bedwin, and Oliver talked happily, Rose told Mr. Brownlow of Nancy's visit.

I have not told Dr. Losberne yet for fear he would rush off and do something foolish. He likes Oliver very much.

I understand, my dear. I will come to your hotel tonight and we will talk.

That night, as soon as Dr. Losberne heard the story, he put on his hat and started for the door.

I'll see every one of them hanged!

Wait, sir! What of finding out about Oliver's parents? Let us talk this over.

It was agreed that Mr. Brownlow and Rose would talk to Nancy to learn more.

Meanwhile, Noah Claypool and Charlotte had come to London. Not long after Oliver had left the coffin-maker's house, they, too, had run away. One night they sat talking at an inn.

Well, we stole the check from the Sowerberrys, but we can't cash it. What will we do here?

A clever man like me can find things to be emptied—pockets, pocketbooks, houses, banks.

Good evening. My name is Fagin. I understand that you would like to do some stealing.

What kind will you do? Taking packages from old ladies?

How about stealing the money mothers give their children?

That's the very thing!

Fagin took Noah and Charlotte to his house.

You'll live like a gentleman here! And you keep half of what you and the lady make.

Just remember that I first take care of Number One—that's me!

Ah, but I'm Number One—because I already know enough about you to have you hanged!

Noah's first job for Fagin was to go to court to check up on Jack Dawkins. The Dodger had been caught stealing.

What is this case?

The boy is a thief, sir. We have a witness.

The Artful Dodger was led away, and Noah reported that he was fine.

Finally it was Sunday night and just about eleven o'clock. Fagin, who was visiting Bill, saw Nancy as she tried to sneak out on her secret errand.

Ah, where's Nancy off to?

I just need some fresh air.

Get back in here! You leave this place, and you'll be sorry!

Back in his own home, Fagin spoke to Noah.

If Nancy leaves Bill, he'll kill her. And if he gets in trouble, we all will. He knows too much.

I'll follow Nancy when she goes out again. I'll tell you what she does.

It was seven days later, the next Sunday night, before Nancy left Bill's.

There she goes. And Bill's out for the night.

She'll never know I'm behind her.

It was just midnight when Nancy met Rose Maylie and Mr. Brownlow on London Bridge. She led them to some stone stairs, where they were not likely to be seen. Noah Claypool hid himself around the corner from them.

I was kept away last Sunday by the man I told the lady about before.

We must find Monks and make him talk.

Nancy told them where to find Monks.

You'll know him by the red mark on his throat.

A red mark like a burn? I think I know the man!

Mr. Brownlow and Rose tried to make Nancy come with them to start a new life.

At least let us give you money.

No, lady. Just give me your handkerchief. Bless you. Good night.

Noah rushed back to Fagin with his news. Fagin sent for Bill Sikes at once.

Suppose someone peached on us?

I'd murder him.

Fagin told Bill about Nancy's meeting on London Bridge. He woke Noah to tell the story again.

She told them she was kept home by Bill—the man she had told them of before.

You was watched tonight. Every word you said was heard! You peached on me!

Bill hit Nancy over the head with a club. As she fell back, trying to stop the bleeding with Rose's handkerchief, Sikes hit her again. Soon she was dead.

For the rest of the night Bill Sikes did not move, but sat looking at Nancy's dead body. Toward morning, he called his dog and ran away.

Whenever he slept, he had nightmares, so he kept walking. Coming across a house on fire, he helped the crowd put it out, glad to get away from his thoughts.

Come and share some food.

Say, have you heard that the killer is around here? The police are looking for him.

Bill did not wait to hear any more.

I must go back to London—and Fagin. But they're looking for me *and* the dog. I must get rid of the dog.

Something about Bill's manner warned the dog. It growled and ran off. Bill set out for London alone.

Not long afterward, Mr. Brownlow stepped from a coach and went into his house. He was followed by Harry Maylie and the coachman, pulling a man between them. The man was Monks.

How dare you take me here? You, who were my father's best friend?

You are free to go. But the minute you do, these men will have the police arrest you. Or, Edward Leeford— you may sit and listen to me.

The two men left as Monks sat down. Mr. Brownlow then told his guest a true story.

"Your father, forced into an unhappy marriage, left your mother when you were about twelve."

"Later he had to go to Rome on business, leaving behind a young lady whom he loved. Her name was Agnes Fleming."

As Mr. Brownlow continued with his story, Monks became very upset.

Your father left with me a picture of the young lady Agnes. In Rome, he became ill. You and your mother got there the day before he died.

Soon afterward, Agnes had a child, Oliver. Most of your father's money should have gone to *him*!

You can't prove anything!

"The only things that can prove who Oliver really is have been thrown into the river," you told Fagin. Every word you spoke was overheard.

You must sign a paper telling the truth about Oliver's parents. And you must give him back the money his father left for him, or I will hand you over to the police.

All right. I will do anything you want.

Because of the murder, the police were also after Fagin and his gang.

Fagin and Noah Claypool were arrested. Charley Bates and Toby Crackit escaped up a chimney.

Soon after the police had gone. . . .

Oh, no! It's Bill Sikes! He's crazy!

When Charley started screaming, Sikes grabbed a rope and climbed onto the roof. He tied one end of the rope around a chimney. He tied the other end to fit under his arms. Suddenly he looked behind him.

It's that dream again! Nancy keeps looking at me!

Sikes slipped, and all of a sudden the rope was around his neck. He had hanged himself!

Two days later, Oliver and his friends were in a hotel room in the town where Oliver was born. Mr. Brownlow brought Monks in to tell his tale.

So! Oliver is your half-brother —the son of Edwin Leeford, your father, and the beautiful Agnes Fleming.

Yes. Agnes died in the workhouse when Oliver was born.

At this moment, Mr. Grimwig entered with Mr. and Mrs. Bumble.

That's the woman who sold me Agnes' locket and ring. She stole them from a nurse—who had already stolen them from the dead Agnes.

That's a lie!

Mr. Grimwig then opened the door to admit two old women. They were the ones who had cared for old Sally.

You shut the door, but we heard you through the cracks.

As Mrs. Bumble and the old nurses left, Mr. Bumble tried to tell Mr. Brownlow that he was not guilty of anything.

But you *are* guilty, Mr. Bumble. The law says that a wife acts under the orders of her husband.

Then the law doesn't know my wife!

When the door closed behind Mr. Bumble, Monks continued his story.

In Rome, my mother burned a will and a letter to Agnes. The will left most of my father's money to Agnes and her child.

From the address on the letter, Mother traced the Flemings to Wales. But Agnes had left, and Mr. Fleming had died.

The father of the unhappy Agnes had *two* daughters. What of the other daughter, the child on his knee?

When Mr. Fleming died, they gave the child to some poor people.

My mother told them lies about the child. But when my mother died, I found that Mrs. Maylie had taken the girl away.

Rose was so surprised by what Monks had said that she could say nothing.

To me she will always by my dear sweet niece!

Then Rose is my aunt! But I can't call you that, dear Rose. You're more like a sister.

The group sat talking together long after Monks had left. When Harry Maylie arrived, he asked to speak with Rose alone.

Have you heard the news?

Yes, dear Rose. But I have come today again to ask you to marry me.

Ah, Harry. There is no problem with my family now, but. . . .

Wait. Hear me out. I have been studying for a new job.

In the lovely English countryside is a small village church. I am to be the minister there.

Dear Harry, I *do* love you. I will be happy to share such a life with you.

Hearing the news, their friends were also very happy.

Meanwhile, Fagin had been sentenced to be hanged.

Very late the night before he was to die, Mr. Brownlow and Oliver went to visit Fagin. He seemed to be losing his mind.

Fagin, you have some papers given to you by Monks. We need them.

Let me go nearer. I am not afraid.

They're in a bag in the front room chimney.

He is an evil man, but I feel sorry for him.

Dawn was breaking. A crowd was already gathering around a scaffold. Oliver held tightly to Mr. Brownlow's hand as they pushed past the people and hurried home.

There had been many changes since Oliver had worked for Fagin. Nancy had been murdered. Sikes had hanged himself. The Dodger was in jail.

Charley Bates was so upset by Sikes' crime that he decided to turn honest. He became a cowherd in Northhamptonshire.

Mr. and Mrs. Bumble lost their jobs. They finally became so poor that they ended up in the very workhouses they had once been in charge of.

Ah, if only I were still the beadle!

Monks had been given part of Oliver's money, but it was soon gone. Returning to his evil ways, he was caught and died in prison.

Rose and Harry were married in the little village church. They moved into the minister's house next door and asked Mrs. Maylie to live with them.

Come see the new flower beds. Oliver helped me plant them.

Dr. Losberne and Mr. Grimwig became good friends. Being lonely in Chertsey, they moved into a cottage near the Maylies.

Every Sunday they went to church.

A very good sermon—but of course I couldn't tell him so.

What shall we do today?

Let's get Oliver and go fishing.

And Oliver? No one was happier than he. Mr. Brownlow adopted him. Then Mr. Brownlow, Oliver, and Mrs. Bedwin moved into a cottage near the Maylies' church. Oliver studied and played and visited his dear friends.

Giles and Brittles slept at the Maylies' house. But they so divided their time among their friends that the villagers never did learn just where they lived.

And on the altar of the old village church was placed a white marble tablet with but one word on it: Agnes.

THE END

COMPLETE LIST OF POCKET CLASSICS AVAILABLE

CLASSICS

COMPLETE LIST OF POCKET CLASSICS AVAILABLE
(cont'd)

C47 The Sea Wolf
C48 The Swiss Family Robinson
C49 Billy Budd
C50 Crime and Punishment
C51 Don Quixote
C52 Great Expectations
C53 Heidi
C54 The Illiad
C55 Lord Jim
C56 The Mutiny on Board H.M.S. Bounty
C57 The Odyssey
C58 Oliver Twist
C59 Pride and Prejudice
C60 The Turn of the Screw

SHAKESPEARE

S 1 As You Like It
S 2 Hamlet
S 3 Julius Caesar
S 4 King Lear
S 5 Macbeth
S 6 The Merchant of Venice
S 7 A Midsummer Night's Dream
S 8 Othello
S 9 Romeo and Juliet
S10 The Taming of the Shrew
S11 The Tempest
S12 Twelfth Night